Disney

P9-CEL-213

Best♥Loved
Classics

pi kids ® publications international, ltd.

Ready to fly to Never Land? First see if you can find these items in the nursery.

Pirate hat

Pirate bandana

Toy pirate sword

Treasure map

Costume headdress

"Hook's hook"

Have you ever seen an elephant fly? Soar with Dumbo and find these circus items.

Bag of popcorn

Drink cup

Clown shoe

This balloon

Cotton candy

Top hat

Ice cream cone

Have a cup of tea with Alice and the Mad Hatter! Look for these mad tea party essentials.

This teacup

This butter knife

This teapot

This jar of jam

This sugar bowl

This spoon

There's nothing the Tramp likes more than chasing chickens! See if you can find all these chicken feathers.

Light brown feather

Brown and white spotted feather

Black feather

Gray feather

Dark brown feather

Black and white spotted feather

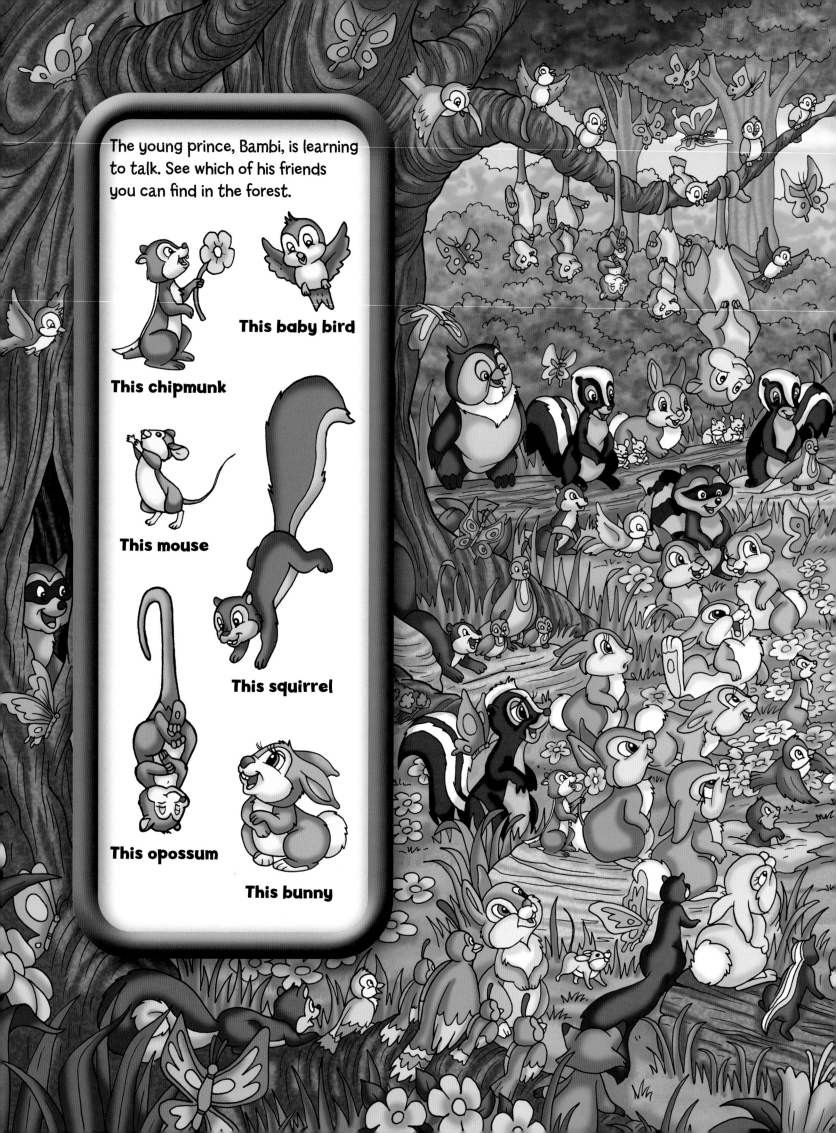

The young prince, Bambi, is learning to talk. See which of his friends you can find in the forest.

This chipmunk

This baby bird

This mouse

This squirrel

This opossum

This bunny

Geppetto wished upon a star and his dream came true! See if you can find these items around Pinocchio and Geppetto.

Pinocchio's school book

Geppetto's night cap

Jiminy Cricket's umbrella

Honest John's cane

The Blue Fairy's wand

Lampwick's slingshot

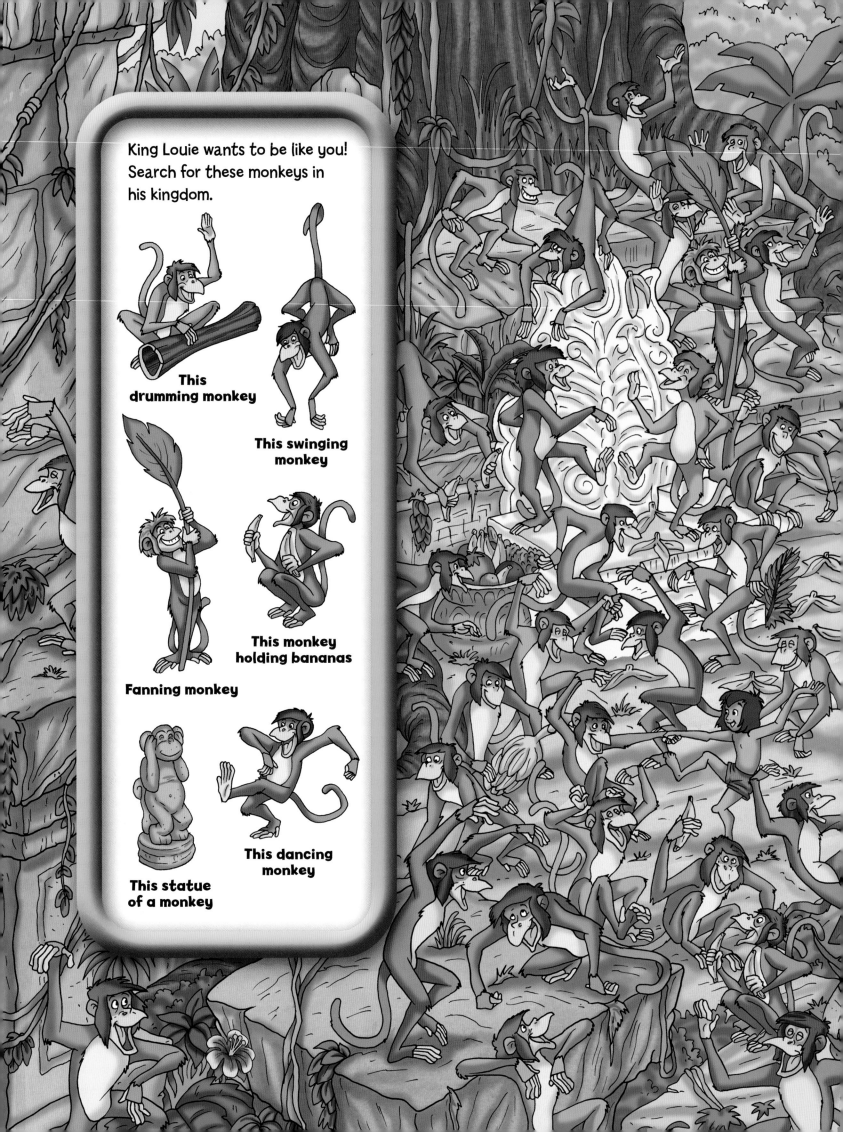

King Louie wants to be like you! Search for these monkeys in his kingdom.

This drumming monkey

This swinging monkey

Fanning monkey

This monkey holding bananas

This statue of a monkey

This dancing monkey

It's a regular Dalmatian plantation in Roger and Anita's apartment. Can you find these six Dalmatians among the hundred and one?

Find these blocks in the nursery that spell "Peter Pan."

Go back to the big top and see if you can find all 20 peanuts.

Climb back through the rabbit hole and look for these Wonderland items.

Hookah pipe

Pocket watch

"Eat Me" candy

Crown

Pipe

"Drink Me" bottle

Scepter

Can you find these chicks hiding around the coop?

Thump your way back to Bambi's forest and look for these butterflies.

See if you can find these musical items in Geppetto's workshop.

Accordion

Lute

Violin

Horn

Cymbals

Street grinder

See if you can find these jungle plants around the ancient ruins.

Banana tree

Palm leaf

Fig tree

Mangrove tree

Hibiscus flower

Violet orchid

Can you find these Dalmatian dog tags?

Heart tag

Diamond tag

Bone tag

Square tag

Star tag

Circle tag